Where Is the Fox?

by Dina McClellan • Illustrated by Ronda Krum

SCHOLASTIC INC.

New York Toronto London Auckland Sydney

Who left this print?

A fox!

It is wet here.

His pads left a print.

What is in there?

A fox!

This gray fox hid in the log.

Who went in there?

It is a fox with lots of fur.
This is his den.

His fur is like his den.
They are the same color.

Who is there?

It is a kit fox.

His fur is like the sand.
They are the same color.

Why are there lots of prints?

There are lots of foxes!
This big red fox is with her pups.

Can you add up the pups?

Is there one pup?

Are there ten pups?

There are six pups.

One pup is still in the den.

Can you see his legs?

What do the pups see?

14

They see a fox!

He has come back to his den.

His pups will get fed.

They will get big!

Phonics Reader 10 ★ Words to Sound Out

/g/*g*	/ks/*x*	/e/*e*	-en	-et
get	fox	den	den	get
big	six	fed	ten	wet
legs		get	went	
log		left		
		legs		
		red		
		wet		

Phonics Reader 10 ★ Words to Remember

her his one this why

Phonics Reader 10 ★ Story Words

color fur gray same